G000146460

10-6-2001

To

Lily
With Love

From

Barbar and
Gramgram.

Walk slowly through the year,
for every day is holy.

The illustrations in this book were selected from
The Lion Treasury of Children's Prayers, published by
Lion Publishing in 1999

Written and compiled by Lois Rock
Illustrations copyright © 1999 Alison Jay
This edition copyright © 2003 Lion Publishing

The moral rights of the compiler and illustrator
have been asserted

Published by
Lion Publishing plc
Mayfield House, 256 Banbury Road,
Oxford OX2 7DH, England
www.lion-publishing.co.uk
ISBN 0 7459 4639 9

First edition 2003
10 9 8 7 6 5 4 3 2 1 0

Acknowledgments
All unattributed prayers by Lois Rock,
copyright © Lion Publishing. 'The God
of love' by Sophie Piper copyright © Lion
Publishing.

A catalogue record for this book is available
from the British Library

Typeset in 15/19 Venetian 301
Printed and bound in Singapore

A Calendar
of
Prayers
for the seasons
of the year

LION
Children's Books

O thought I!
What a beautiful thing
God has made winter to be
by stripping the trees
and letting us see
their shapes and forms.
What a freedom does it seem
to give to the storms.

Dorothy Wordsworth (1771–1855)

God, who made the earth,
The air, the sky, the sea,
Who gave the light its birth,
Careth for me.

God, who made all things,
On earth, in air, in sea,
Who changing seasons brings,
Careth for me.

Sarah Betts Rhodes (c. 1870)

The whole bright world rejoices now:
with laughing cheer! with boundless joy!
The birds do sing on every bough:
Alleluia!

Then shout beneath the racing skies:
with laughing cheer! with boundless joy!
To him who rose that we might rise:
Alleluia!

God, Father, Son and Holy Ghost:
with laughing cheer! with boundless joy!
Our God most high, our joy, our boast:
Alleluia!

Easter carol (seventeenth century)

God bless the seeds we scatter
And send the cool grey rain
To mix up with the sunshine
And bring us flowers again.

When I see the birds go soaring,
wheeling, dipping through the sky,

Deep inside my spirit
longs to learn to fly.

For flowers that bloom about our feet,
Father, we thank Thee,
For tender grass so fresh and sweet,
Father, we thank Thee,
For the song of bird and hum of bee,
For all things fair we hear or see,
Father in heaven, we thank Thee.

For blue of stream and blue of sky,
Father, we thank Thee,
For pleasant shade of branches high,
Father, we thank Thee,
For fragrant air and cooling breeze,
For beauty of the blooming trees,
Father in heaven, we thank Thee.

For this new morning with its light,
Father, we thank Thee,
For rest and shelter of the night,
Father, we thank Thee.
For health and food, for love and friends,
For everything thy goodness sends,
Father in heaven, we thank Thee.

Ralph Waldo Emerson (1803–82)

God is out walking in the clear blue morning,
when the birds trill their melodies.

God is out walking in the bright gold daytime,
when the butterflies shimmer among the grasses.

God is out walking in the warm mauve evening,
when the shadows melt into the twilight.

God is out walking in the cool silver night,
when the stars curve across the heavens.

God is out walking when I am out walking.
God is there walking beside me.

The golden sand,
the silver tide,
the clear blue sky
where seagulls glide;
the lazy hours
of rest and play:
we thank God
for our holiday.

All thanks to God
for the harvest of the orchard;

All thanks to God
for the harvest of the field;

All thanks to God
for the harvest of the garden;

All thanks to God
for the earth and all its yield.

For all the rich autumnal glories spread –
The flaming pageant of the ripening woods,
The fiery gorse, the heather-purpled hills;
The rustling leaves that fly before the wind

And lie below the hedgerows whispering;
For meadows silver-white with hoary dew;
The first crisp breath of wonder in the air,
We thank you, Lord.

Anonymous

In the grey time of the evening
In the grey time of the year
May God bring us home in safety
May God keep us without fear.

God, our loving Father, help us remember the birth of Jesus, that we may share in the song of the angels, the gladness of the shepherds and the wisdom of the wise men.

Close the door of hate and open the door of love all over the world.

Let kindness come with every gift and good desires with every greeting.

Deliver us from evil by the blessing which Christ brings and teach us to be merry with clean hearts.

May the Christmas morning make us happy to be your children and the Christmas evening bring us to our beds with grateful thoughts, forgiving and forgiven, for Jesus' sake. Amen.

Robert Louis Stevenson (1850–94)